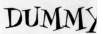

DUMMY

and

John Mole is one of today's leading poets: his
children's collection *Boo to a Goose* won the Signal
Award in 1988, and his work for adults won a
Cholmondeley Award in 1994. A teacher for many
years, he has also edited for a small press, compiled
and presented feature programmes for the BBC,
and plays regularly as a jazz clarinettist. He now
writes full-time and has currently been appointed
'Poet in the City' by The Poetry Society. John Mole
is married to the artist Mary Norman, who has
provided the delightful illustrations for this book.

JOHN MOLE

★

THE DUMMY'S DILEMMA
and Other Poems

Illustrations by Mary Norman

Hodder
Children's
Books

a division of Hodder Headline plc

Contents

The Lesson   7

The Dummy's Dilemma   8

Time to Get Up   10

The Invisible Man   12

The Door   14

The Song of Abner Brown   15

A Riddle   22

Miss Lowman-Lang   23

Black Jack   25

The Coastguard   28

Hamlet's Counting Rhyme   30

A November Riddle   32

The Coleridge Show   34

A Lesson Taught by Kites   36

Old London Town   38

Pig in the Middle   39

Halloween   40

The Model   42

Mr. Yo   44

A Bad Night   46

At the Swimming Pool   47

The Jolly Gentleman   48

Cold Shoulder   49
Coventry   50
Ten Full Bottles   52
Sometimes   55
Gnomic   56
Gliders   57
She Heard Them Shouting   58
Exactly   60
A Tall Story   61
Stretching The Point   64
This is the Week   65
Christmas Crackers   66
The Pong   67
Olé   68
Doctor Samuel Johnson Consults
  His Dictionary Upon Being Stung
  By A Critic   70
i.m. Jim   71
The Last Abbot Sings To His
  Favourite Piglet   72
Carnival Song   74
Uncle Ray   75

*To all the children
I have been working with
in Hackney and Tower Hamlets.*

The Lesson

'How do you draw?' they asked.
His answer: 'I take my line for a walk.'

What did he mean?

He meant:
'Give me paper,
give me a pencil.
Watch'.

'What shall I write?' you ask.
My answer: 'Take your line for a walk.'

What do I mean?

Here's paper,
here's a pencil,
here will be the world
as nobody else has seen it.

Believe me,
I mean it.

The Dummy's Dilemma

I sit here on your knee
And look up at your face.
I think I know I'm me
But best check just in case.

I look up at your face.
I'm sure your lips are sealed
But best check just in case
Our secret is revealed.

I'm sure your lips are sealed.
You won't give me away.
Our secret is revealed
If one word goes astray.

You won't give me away
As long as I behave.
If one word goes astray...
My situation's grave.

As long as I behave
I sit here on your knee.
My situation's grave.
I *think* I know I'm me.

Time to Get Up

This is the mirror beside my bed.

This is the face I see in the morning,
Every feature, the whole lot yawning,
In the mirror beside my bed.

These are the eyes, all sticky and drowsy,
That peep through the messed hair, rumpled, mousy,
That falls on the face I see in the morning,
Every feature, the whole lot yawning,
In the mirror beside my bed.

There go the dreams, already fading
As thoughts of the day begin invading
Those half-open eyes, all sticky and drowsy,
That peep through the messed hair, rumpled, mousy,
That falls on the face I see in the morning,
Every feature, the whole lot yawning,
In the mirror beside my bed.

Here come shrill voices calling upstairs,
The sounds of the day and its many affairs
That banish those dreams, already fading,
As thought upon thought begins invading
Those half-open eyes, all sticky and drowsy,
That peep through the messed hair, rumpled, mousy,
That falls on the face I see in the morning,
Every feature, the whole lot yawning,
In the mirror beside my bed.

'Your breakfast is cold, you're going to be late,
The cat's on the table and licking your plate!'
And so on, etcetera, calling upstairs,
The same every day, the usual affairs
With no time for dreams reluctantly fading
As light gets impatient but goes on invading
My half-open eyes, all sticky and drowsy,
That peep through the messed hair, rumpled, mousy,
That falls on the face I see in the morning,
Every feature, the whole lot yawning
Without being given quite enough warning
Or time to get used to another day dawning
In the mirror beside my bed.

The Invisible Man

The invisible man is a joker
Who wears an invisible grin
And the usual kind of visible clothes
Which cover up most of him,

But there's nothing above his collar
Or at the end of his sleeves,
And his laughter is like the invisible wind
Which rustles the visible leaves.

When the visible storm clouds gather
He strides through the visible rain
In a special invisible see-through cloak
Then invisibly back again.

But he wears a thick, visible overcoat
To go out when it visibly snows
And the usual visible footprints
Get left wherever he goes.

In the visible heat-haze of summer
And the glare of the visible sun,
He undoes his visible buttons
With invisible fingers and thumb,

Takes off his visible jacket,
Loosens his visible tie,
Then snaps his visible braces
As he winks an invisible eye.

Last thing in his visible nightgown
Tucked up in his visible bed
He rests on a visible pillow
His weary invisible head

And ponders by visible moonlight
What invisibility means
Then drifts into silent invisible sleep
Full of wonderful visible dreams.

The Door

I woke as it closed behind me.
Where had I been in my sleep?
Daylight arrived to remind me
That I had a secret to keep.

Who was it trusted my silence?
Who had allowed me to go?
Did that one dream make any difference?
How can I ever know?

Will someone still be waiting
When I'm nothing but thin air?
Shall I knock for a second meeting?
Will a voice call out *Who's there?*

The Song of Abner Brown

This is Abner Brown,
My cat.

He *looks* lazy,
He *looks* fat.

He's good at making
Grumpy faces.

He likes to curl up
In shady places.

When strangers pass
He hears them say:

*There lies a cat
Of yesterday!*

And then he smiles
Because he knows

That there's more to him
Than they suppose.

Although he's many
Cat-years old,

Abner's a cat
Who is UNCONTROLLED.

He may look fat,
He may look lazy

But Abner's good
At going crazy.

He'll let you think
That he's asleep

Then suddenly
He'll make a leap.

Abner becomes
A ball of fur,

A bouncing bomb,
A flying purr.

Before you know it
Already he

Will have reached the top
Of the tallest tree.

He stretches, grins
And thumps his chest.

He thinks he's Tarzan
(Aren't you impressed?).

From branch to branch
He sways and swings

And this is the Abner
Song he sings:

Oh I am a cat
That gets around,

Just try to keep me
On the ground.

I may be old
And dim of eye

But Abner Brown
Was born to fly.

A scaredy cat?
Not me. No chance.

Watch this moggy
Skip and dance.

Tickle my ears
And shake my paw, sir!

Give me my milk
From a flying saucer.

Yesterday's cat
Was born to sorrow

But Abner's a cat
Of today and tomorrow.

Yesterday's cat?
Oh no, no, no.

Abner's a cat
On the go, go, go!

Then he gives his chest
One final thump

And you'd think for a moment
That he's going to jump,

But then my veteran
Abner Brown

Very gingerly
Scrambles down.

For every old cat
However tough

There comes a time
When he's had enough,

When it's wiser perhaps
To admit you're old

Than to go on being
Uncontrolled.

So back he limps
To his shady place

And the grumpy look
Returns to his face,

But he knows that I know
That before too long

He'll be up again
And singing his song.

A Riddle

Mine is the ungloved
pulsing fingertip,

the shroud, the interlace
of brittle leaves.

I am the sculpture of your stiffened
hosepipe's tangle

and a light-scored requiem,
a glittering stave.

Mine is the cruel purity
that snaps all iron,

sends your warm breath
biting backwards.

I am the splintered rainbow
locked in ice,

the broken promise
of an early spring.

(Answer: Frost)

Miss Lowman-Lang

I sat at my desk with a china inkwell
sunk into its hole at the end of the runnel
you picked your pen up from, a twig-thin
wooden shaft with the nib stuck in
like a pigmy's weapon. It was good
for a stab and flick if you were in the mood
and your neighbour wasn't. Then
it was always time for *Settle Down!*
The ink we used was made from a powder
you could thicken into jelly. Our teacher
was Miss Lowman-Lang. She taught us writing,
to use those primitive pens without blotting,
to give each letter's backbone a loop
in the right place so that it linked up
into a chain called *word* which at our age
had little for us to do with language
but a lot with good behaviour.
I was eight (and two plus two was four).
She showed us with her special pen.
Its lever squeezed a tube inside. *Fountain*
she called it, and it used a special ink
from her bottle with a label: *Parker Quink*.
One day, when I was standing at her desk,
I plucked the courage up to ask
if I could hold it. 'Yes of course,' she said
'but do be careful.' Then what I did
was take it (carefully) by the top bit

with the clip on and oh no, the writing part
fell out and arrowed to the floorboards
where its gold nib stuck and quivered.
Everyone saw. Miss Lowman-Lang was kind,
although she couldn't say she didn't mind,
but I was dumbstruck. I could see
the nib was split apart and bent impossibly
beyond repair. I can still hear my fumbled
muttering of guilt, 'I'll take it home to Dad.
My Dad'll know, my Dad'll mend it.'
But, of course, he couldn't and I didn't,
nor was I old enough to say or even think
I'll pay for it although in time's indelible ink
and after fifty years of unforgotten shame
perhaps I'm paying as I write your name,
Miss Lowman-Lang, in joined-up writing.
This poem is for you, Miss Lowman-Lang.

Black Jack

Jack was a pirate
Who couldn't cope
But he liked to polish
His telescope.

While the tall waves crashed
And the loud winds roared,
He'd lie in his cabin
Completely bored.

Oh X he muttered
May mark the spot
But I've seen it all,
I've done the lot.

There's nothing left,
There's nothing new,
Nothing but old lags
For a crew.

If it weren't for the fact
They're as bored as me
I should have on my hands
A mutiny.

Then one calm night,
More mild than cold,
While his crew were snoring
In the hold,

Jack tucked his telescope
Under an arm
(His right was left
But his left long gone)

And climbed to the fo'c's'le
For one last time
As if he knew
I'd be writing this rhyme

And clapped the tube
To his one good eye
And looked at the sea
And looked at the sky

Then hammered his peg-leg
On the deck
As he cursed by jingo,
Jove and heck

There's nothing for me
But the stars overhead,
So I think I'll become
A poet instead.

The Coastguard

Sometimes he asks the waves
as they recur
if there is nothing more
than this, the flat
shine of what is left
by their receding
then the roar
of their return, a come-
back leap
spray-dazzling
on the rocks
to yet another burst
of brief applause.

Their only answer
is the blown fringe
of a frothy curtain
tasselling the shore-line,
and a solitary
gull which struts
across the stage
of its reflection
lifting now one foot
and now the other.

Hamlet's Counting Rhyme

One two
Nothing new

Three four
Life's a bore

Five six
Just for kicks

Seven eight
Let's tempt fate

Nine ten
But then again

Ten nine
Now's not the time

Eight seven
All things being even

Six five
Better alive

Four three
Than eternity

Two one
Since dreams may come

Zero zero
And I'm no hero

A November Riddle

We've lighted Caesar to his bed
And cast his shadow on the wall.

One of our namesakes steamed ahead
But never left the ground at all.

We are the other half of mash
And must be handled carefully.

We're more than just a sudden flash
Though what you hear is what you see.

We can remember when a saint
Went spinning on her wheel of flame.

The sky is a canvas which we paint
And if by now you've guessed our name

Remember while the bonfire roars
To keep all pets shut safe indoors.

The Coleridge Show

Samuel Taylor Coleridge's
Head was full of notions,
Of scholarship, philosophy
And passionate emotions.

Once he was away, it was
Impossible to stop him.
He'd talk and talk and talk and talk.
For talk you couldn't top him.

In fact, it really must be said
If you saw Samuel coming
Then that was probably the time
To turn round and start running.

His friend Charles Lamb, though, didn't
When they met on Hampstead Heath.
Once Samuel got started
He never paused for breath.

Lamb couldn't get a word in
However hard he tried.
Oh the breadth of Samuel's knowledge
Was infinitely wide.

On and on and on he went,
This, that, and so-and-so,
While Lamb stood rooted to the spot.
This was The Coleridge Show.

He listened and he listened,
For punishment a glutton
Then Samuel to stress a point
Tugged at Lamb's waistcoat button.

Off it came, and off went Lamb
Released for his walk at last
But according to one observer
Who later happened past

He saw a fellow, clearly mad,
(So he didn't choose to linger)
Lecturing to a tiny spot
Between his thumb and finger.

A Lesson Taught by Kites

Here on The Downs, our bright two-handers
Zap and clatter, criss-cross, frenzied
In a wind that whips them and knows
Nothing of control. Like scimitars
They slash across each other's flight paths
In a sudden execution of the air, or fall
As if betrayed by their own gaudiness,
A pride of emperors unseated, now again
Ascendant, tugged and lifted for another
Aerial enthronement, splendour
High above the grass, then once more
Dumped down by the wheel of fortune
In their slackened strings, no permanence
For even the most gorgeous, buoyant,
Effortless display. There's nothing we can do
But hold on tight, lean back, pay court
To triumph while it lasts, a flock of little people
Buffeted and scattered on these slopes
As fragments of the world around us
Teach the law that even beauty must obey.

Old London Town

When coppers said 'Ullo, Ullo!'
And crooks exclaimed 'Cor Blimey!',
When toffs appended 'Don't y'know!'
In toppers, silken-shiny,

When cads confessed 'I tell a lie,'
And silly girls believed them,
When nurses shrieked 'Oh my! Oh my!'
If bad behaviour grieved them,

When Little Miss's Good Dog's treat
Was a tasty piece of liver,
There were shadows in the street
And bodies in the river.

Pig in the Middle

I'm pig in the middle
Between two stools,
I sit on the fence
And obey the rules,
I face both ways,
I know the score.
That's what a pig
In the middle is for.

I'm pig in the middle,
I'm yes and no,
I'll come if you call
And I'm willing to go,
I fill the space
Between either / or.
That's what a pig
In the middle is for.

Halloween

Give me ghosts,
Give me ghouls,
October fiends
Not April fools.

I want tricks,
I want treats,
Not sunny fields
But shady streets.

Give me darkness,
Give me dread,
Not sweet green
But sticky red.

I want fire,
I want fangs,
I want whiz
And I want bangs.

Give me skulls,
Give me bones,
Enormous screams
Not little groans.

I want a mask,
I want a cloak,
I want a big black cat
To stroke.

Give me horns
And a swishing tail,
Give me a six inch
Fingernail.

I want a luminous
Skeleton,
I want a broom
To ride upon.

I don't want to be
A sugar-plum fairy,
But I'll want to go home
If it gets too scary.

I'll want warm cocoa
In my special cup,
And I'll want my mum
To tuck me up.

The Model

Definitely not a toy
The ad. said in the B.O.P. *
Which made it just the job for me
So definitely not a boy.

Though some way off from man's estate
And therefore sick of being told
*Perhaps next year. You're not quite old
Enough.* I learned to lie in wait.

A full-scale model had to do,
An imitation of the real,
So definitely not ideal
But good enough to see me through.

A racer with the works inside
Beneath a bonnet that would lift
Became the only sort of gift
To satisfy my secret pride.

* *Boy's Own Paper* (a popular magazine in my youth)

I'd sleep with it beside my bed
And reach to touch it in the dark
Then turn, as from a boundary mark,
To fit the pillow to my head,

To dream of travelling all night
Until my world had fully grown –
So definitely half-way home,
So definitely not there, quite.

Mr. Yo

My name is Mr. Yo.
I'm the great yo-yo master.
I'm ready, steady, go
And always getting faster.

I'm the great yo-yo master.
I'm the best there is
And always getting faster.
Just watch me do the biz.

I'm the best there is
So if you want a thrill
Just watch me do the biz
And envy me my skill.

So if you want a thrill
Forget the tricks you've done
And envy me my skill
Because I'm number one.

Forget the tricks you've done.
I can do everything
Because I'm number one.
I'm magic with the string.

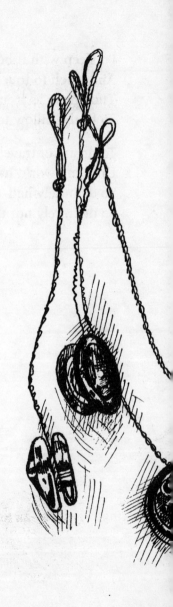

I can do everything.
You might as well pack up.
I'm magic with the string
So I'm bound to win the cup.

You might as well pack up.
My name is Mr. Yo
So I'm bound to win the cup –
I'm ready,
                    stead…
                                Oh no!

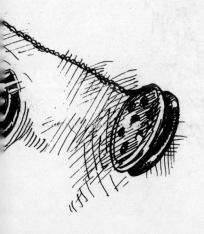

A Bad Night

Full moon up there making a brave fist of it
Through that vague cloud which veils you
Or, moist in the lamp-lit mist of it,
Night's eye weeping too,

Down here, well, much the same,
Things haven't been grand
But I've only myself to blame
As I think you must understand.

At the Swimming Pool

Such a foot-slap hall of echoes
bouncing off each other
wall-to-white-tiled wall
across the water, meeting
midway as a hydra-headed
body of pure scream, falsetto,
fit to raise the roof
and cry blue murder.

Such a palace of parabola
and belly-flop, the perfect
cleaving plunge, the dead-weight
ignominious tumble's
loss of balance, such a field
of folk afloat, a spray-blessed
bobbing, winged and ringed
and skull-capped holiday.

But such, for some, a mayhem
of distraction, these the serious ones,
the steady back-and-forthers
measuring their lengths, intent
on nothing but the next
completed turn, the adding up
to yet another more than yesterday
and with a privacy of purpose all their own.

The Jolly Gentleman

I say I say
I say what what
what what
I say I say

I am a jolly
gentleman
and I bid you all
good day

Cold Shoulder

'I say,' he said,
'I say, I say,
When I walk past
You turn away.'

'Come on,' he said,
'Come on, come on,
Is it something
I've done wrong?'

'Look here,' he said,
'Look here, look here,
This can't go on,
It isn't fair.'

'Oh well,' he said,
'Oh well, oh well,
If you won't
Be sensible...'

This was forty
Years ago.
Why it happened
I don't know

Or could it be
I won't admit
That I might have been
The cause of it?

Coventry

'Send her to Coventry' they said
'And if you talk to her you're dead.
If she even looks your way
Turn around and make her pay.

If she asks you what she's done
Walk off slowly (never run),
If she calls out after you
Let her, till her face turns blue.

If she takes you by surprise
Blank her out with stony eyes,
If her tears begin to flow
Make sure that she knows you know.

If she finds you after school
Don't go soft and break the rule,
If she sees you, try to hide
Or pass by on the other side.'

So that is how it was, and then
Things were normal once again
But she'll recall for evermore
The town where no one talked to her.

Ten Full Bottles

Ten full bottles
Standing in a line.
Pour one over Peter
Then there will be nine.

Nine full bottles.
Peter can't wait
To sprinkle his on Suzy.
That leaves eight.

Eight full bottles.
Plenty more to go.
A drip drip drop for David.
Seven of them now!

Seven full bottles.
Just watch Kirsty fix
A waterfall for William
And that makes six.

Six full bottles.
Duck and dodge and dive.
Flicking froth at Fergus
Leaves just five.

Five full bottles.
Someone keep the score.
Happy birthday Benjamin.
Now there are four.

Four full bottles.
Let the next one be
A gorgeous gush for Gemma
To make it three.

Three full bottles.
Nearly time for you,
But first a shake at Sharon
Then that just leaves two.

Two full bottles.
Standing side by side…

Look out, someone's coming.
I think we'd better hide.

Sometimes

Sometimes the mischief of your grin
Is the label on a box with nothing in.

Sometimes the furrow of your frown
Is misery smiling upside-down.

Sometimes the hammer of your laugh
Is enough to split my world in half.

Sometimes you simply wait to see
Which of your tricks work best on me.

Gnomic

I am the oldest known gnome,
No gnome is older than me,
I am the oldest known gnome
Though an unknown gnome there may be.

An unknown gnome there may be
But nobody knows of him yet
Therefore no gnome is older than me
So give me a little respect.

Gliders

Hoist them up, let go
The rope, just so
They hang there
Balancing on air.

The Sunday sky
Is suddenly
Full of them, their slim
Bodies, delicate and trim.

Such an intense,
Mysterious silence,
Such a slow, weightless,
Gradual progress.

Almost they repose
Above their own shadows,
Almost they keep
Watch over their own sleep,

Until with a sudden
Wakeful dipping down
They seem
As if snatched from a dream

To obey once more
The weekday law
Of nose to the ground,
Deadweight, earthbound.

She Heard Them Shouting

She heard them shouting at each other
Through her bedroom wall
But that was how it often was,
Nothing unusual.

She could never make out their words
Or begin to guess
Exactly what it was this time
Might have started the mess.

Once she lay awake
The whole night through,
Wondering what if anything
She could do.

Were they asleep yet,
Would it start again,
Would it be even louder
Or just the same?

She'd heard them shouting at each other
Through her bedroom wall
And now this silent waiting
Was worst of all.

Exactly

Whatever happened yesterday
it wasn't me, exactly,
wasn't you, exactly,
wasn't anyone, exactly,
but this morning
nothing is the same.

Whatever either said
it wasn't true, exactly,
wasn't lies, exactly,
wasn't meant, exactly,
but between the two of us
we're both to blame.

Whatever started it
it wasn't right, exactly,
wasn't wrong, exactly,
wasn't playing fair, exactly,
but the rules were missing
when we found the game.

Whatever happens next
it won't be now, exactly,
won't be yet, exactly,
won't be what it was, exactly,
but at least it may be something
we can give a name.

A Tall Story

Yesterday Miss Williams told the class
'Use your imagination!
Everybody, close their eyes
(you too, Sophie).
Now what can you see?'

'Miss,' said Sophie, grinning,
'there's a baby alligator
lying on your desk.
He likes you, look,
his legs are waving in the air.
I think he wants his tummy tickled.'

'Well done, Sophie.
Excellent. Thank you. Everybody
open your eyes now.'
So we did.

And there he was, the alligator,
just like Sophie said,
and when Miss Williams
had tickled him enough she popped him
head-down in her handbag
with his scaley, waving
tail-tip sticking out.

'See you later, pet,'
she said,
'but, children, that's enough of that.
Pick up your pencils, now,
it's time to write.'…

At break-time, all of us
went up to Sophie
as she stood there, gobsmacked,
like a conjuror's assistant
who had managed her own trick.
'Sophie, you're brilliant,'
we told her.
'Wait till you hear *our* stories.'…

Later, back home,
my Mum, as usual, asked me
what I'd done today at school
and (when I told her) just for once
she didn't say *'That Sophie!'* like she always did
but simply

'You and your imagination!'

Stretching the Point

Give me something difficult to do. That
was far too easy. I need to be stretched
is what my report says. If I was stretched
I wouldn't be so difficult. What's this?
I can't do that. Impossible. I promise you
that's stretching it too far. I tell you what,
you're going to have a problem on your hands,
your problem. Solving it will not be easy.
It will stretch you. Why be so diffficult?
This can't be what you need. So come on,
what's your problem? Give me my report.
You can't do that? Sometimes I think
you can't do anything. Hey, take it easy!

This is the Week

This is the week when you can hear a pin drop
but mustn't pick it up, when all the facts
stand to attention and you gaze in panic
at their unfamiliar faces. This is the week
when everyone seems to write faster
than you do and asks for more paper, when
the back of your friend's head is giving
nothing away that is any use. This
is the week of the surreptitious cough,
the pen that runs out, the staggered
dash to the toilet, the watched clock's
ruthless handiwork. This is the week
of the swot's apotheosis, the rebel's
bottoming-out, the cheat's come-uppance
and the teachers' unreadable minds
as their eyes meet yours. Then this
is the term that is almost over
except for the lists, the tall form order,
the praise, the blame, the could-do-better
which nevertheless are of less account
than a life to be lived and summer waiting.

Christmas Crackers

A cellophane fish curling up in the palm of your hand,
A trick with instructions that even your father will not
   understand.

All manner of marvels that wriggle and wobble and hop,
The whistle you blow until everything comes to a stop.

Pellets which blossom in water or burst into flame,
Invisible ink to be heated, revealing your name,

A paper hat flimsily slipping down over your eyes,
A ring quite unsuited to fingers of all but diminutive
   size…

These are the little ones, seasonal gimcracks at most
But precious for being just that and so easily lost.

The Pong

It might have come from Peter,
It might have come from Dean,
But when they stood together
It was sort of in between.

It smelt a bit like armpits,
It smelt a bit like feet,
And if either walked away
It was sort of incomplete.

Olé

(Picasso: The Three Musicians)

This is the picture of we three,
The Maestro, Carlos and me,
when we all dressed up
in Pablo's wardrobe for a trip
to Dreamland. Can't you just hear
the music as if you were there
with its squeezebox of notes
at full stretch, the clarinet's
chalumeau tootle, the gold guitar,
and our six feet thumping the floor,
olé, and Conchita's making eight
as she brought us each a heaped plate
of steaming paella. Oh it was great
with Pablo urging us on – *More! More!* –
until the neighbours hammered at the door
and we let them in. Then we all took bets
on how many days and nights
we could keep it up, this being without a care
in the world, this wish-you-were-here
rumpus of happiness, this non-stop
once-in-a-lifetime letting-rip
of The Maestro, Carlos and me
in Pablo's picture of we three.

Doctor Samuel Johnson Consults His Dictionary Upon Being Stung By A Critic

Rascal, rapscallion,
runagate, recreant,
reprobate, ruffian,
reptilian wretch,
cockatrice, cullion,
castaway, caitiff,
conscienceless, capital
catch for Jack Ketch,
libertine, loafer,
lickspittle, lacklustre,
loveless laggard,
lumbering loon,
sesquipedalian
scapegrace, scoundrel,
suffer my syntax
and suffocate soon!

i.m. Jim

Jim, Jim,
Double-dare Jim
Was an absolute menace
To life and limb,
But then to play safe
He had a whim
So nothing much more
Was heard of him.

The Last Abbot Sings To His Favourite Piglet

Pink-skinned, scrubbed
And slippery one,
My squealing runt
Of a singleton,

From the straw-lined cradle
In your sty
You will come to glory
By and by.

The cock will crow,
The sun will shine,
Oh new little, true little
Pig of mine.

When the world has wound up
Its affairs,
I shall remember you
In my prayers.

Carnival Song

Hoisted higher than us all
On your daddy's shoulders, girl.

Here is a world to see,
Here is your community.

Look out, look down,
Cry big love, spread it around.

Make it so we laugh with you,
Make old sadness pack and go.

This is everybody's street,
These are tomorrow's dancing feet.

All the colours, every skin,
A whole new life to be dressed in.

On your daddy's shoulders, girl, ride high,
Apple of our future's eye.

Uncle Ray

'Don't be such a solemn owl,'
said Uncle Ray,
my father's younger brother,
when he found me sitting indoors
reading on *a lovely sunny day*.

He tried to shame me
into sunlight: 'Come on, Four-eyes,
spread your wings a bit
old sport, old fruit!'

but I just sat there, beak down
buried in my book
and didn't give a hoot.

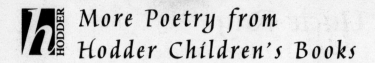
HOT AIR

Poems by

JOHN MOLE

**Words come out like stars sometimes
and choose the darkest nights to sparkle in...**

Signal Poetry Award-winner, John Mole, looks at
everyday things and writes magical poetry to send
shivers down the spine. The poems in HOT AIR
will make you think, laugh and cry...

**More Poetry from
Hodder Children's Books**

DEAR FUTURE...
A TIME CAPSULE
OF POEMS
Selected by
DAVID ORME

To the future person who finds these poems – greetings!
We often try to imagine what you'll be like.
Do you ever wonder about us?

This book will tell you of all the special things in
our world today: Good things – like hanging out,
fishing, TV and trees. Bad things – like the dentist,
wet sports days, traffic jams and homework.

Is your life so different?
Maybe you can time travel back and tell us?

**Poets include: Wendy Cope, Pheobe Hesketh,
Wes Magee, John Mole and Brian Moses!**

CHOOSE YOUR SUPERHERO

Poems by

NORMAN SILVER

Are you ready for a world of imagination, where all the rules are broken, where ancient earth magic is uncovered – and you are drenched in flower showers?

Here you will find yourself initiated into a secret, fire-scaled clan, then watch in horror as your best friend grows talons and fangs. You may even be called upon to save the world!

Dare you accept the challenge? Then you may begin…

h HODDER

More Poetry from Hodder Children's Books

THE COMPLETE POETICAL WORKS OF PHEOBE FLOOD

Introduced by

JOHN WHITWORTH

In Phoebe Flood and her poetical works, John Whitworth views the world through the eyes of a 10-year old with this fine collection.

Dealing with subjects close to all ten-year old hearts, Pheobe expresses herself through plays, lists and just plain and simple verse. Here is a collection to amuse, to relate to, and to savour...

THE LAST OF THE WALLENDAS AND OTHER POEMS

RUSSELL HOBAN

In this carefully crafted collection you will find
poems to surprise and delight…

Be ready to watch someone vanish in a hall of
mirrors, glimpse a ghost galloping flame-like
through the night, and learn a sinister secret
locked fathoms beneath the sea…

Witty, wise and funny, sometimes chillingly
dark, and beautifully complemented by
Patrick Benson's magical illustrations, these
poems will be relished by all.